570

FRIENDS

D1430834

On Four Feet

ARTHUR I. GATES
MIRIAM BLANTON HUBER
FRANK SEELY SALISBURY

THE MACMILLAN COMPANY : NEW YORK

Illustrated by CHARLES PAYZANT AND ASSOCIATES
HELEN HANSEN, SYLVIA HOLLAND, JANET PAGE,
BASIL DAVIDOVICH, ERNEST TERRAZAS

Acknowledgments

Grateful acknowledgment is made to the following publishers
and authors for permission to use copyrighted material:

E. P. Dutton & Co., Inc., New York, for "Jump or Jiggle," by
Evelyn Beyer, from *Another Here and Now Story Book*, edited
by Lucy Sprague Mitchell; published and copyrighted, 1937, by
E. P. Dutton & Co., Inc., New York.

Houghton Mifflin Company for "Baby Monkey and the Elephant," adapted by permission from *Baby Orang and Junior*, by
Katharine K. Garbutt; copyright, 1944, by Katharine K. Garbutt and Bernard Garbutt.

Copyright, 1951, by The Macmillan Company. All Rights Reserved.

Second Printing 1952

PRINTED IN UNITED STATES OF AMERICA

Stories

3

Boys and Girls

Little Dog

"Oh, Ted!" said Sally.
"I see something coming.
Do you see it?"

"Yes, I do," said Ted.
"What is it?
What is it, Sally?"

"Oh, now I can see!"
said Sally.
"It is a little dog.
It is a little puppy.
Come here, puppy!
Look, Ted.
Look at the little puppy."

7

"Here, here, puppy!" said Ted.
"Where are you going?"

"He is a little, little puppy,"
said Sally.
"Where is he going?"

"Now, now, puppy!" said Ted.
"Come here, puppy.
We like dogs."

"My, my!" said Sally.
"See how little he is!"

"Have you a home, little dog?"
said Ted.
"Where is your home?"

"Oh, little puppy!" said Sally.
"Where is your home?"

9

Boy and Girl

"Look, Ted!" said Sally.
"Here come a boy and a girl."

The boy and girl ran up
to Ted and Sally.

"Is this your dog?" said Ted.

"Oh, yes!" said the girl.
"He is my dog.
He ran away.
We looked and looked.
Oh, thank you! Thank you!"

"This is Sally," said Ted.
"And I am Ted."

"I am Jean," said the girl.
"I am Bruce," said the boy.

"We like your dog," said Sally.

"Yes," said Jean.
"He is a good little puppy.
But he did run away."

"Ted, do you have a dog?"
said Bruce.

"Oh, yes!" said Ted.
"I have Boots.
Come and see Boots."

"Come, Jean," said Sally.
"Come and see Boots.
I want you to see Tuffy, too.
Tuffy is my cat."

Friends

Ted and Sally
and Bruce and Jean
went to the play house.
Boots was there.

"Come here, Boots," said Ted.
"Come and see the little dog."

The puppy ran to Boots.
He wanted to play with Boots.
Boots wanted to play, too.

"They will be friends," said Ted.
"They will play and have fun.
Boots wants a friend."

"Jean," said Sally.
"Look up on the play house.
There is my cat, Tuffy.
Come down and play, Tuffy.
Come down and make friends
with Jean."

But Tuffy did not come down.
He looked at the boys and girls.
He looked at the dogs.
But he did not come down.

14

"I will get my dolls, Jean,"
said Sally.
"We will play with the dolls."

"I will get my wagon," said Ted.
"Bruce and I will play with it."

Jean and Sally played
with the dolls.
Bruce and Ted played
with the wagon.
Boots played with the puppy.
They played and played.

15

Tuffy looked down
at Boots and the puppy.
Tuffy wanted to play, too.
Down he came.
Away he ran
to play with the dogs.

"Oh, Sally!" said Jean.
"There is Tuffy.
He wants to be friends
with my little dog.
See Tuffy run and play."

16

"Here comes Mother," said Sally.
"Mother, this is Jean.
And this is Bruce.
Jean and Bruce are new friends."

"How do you do, Jean?"
said Mother.
"How do you do, Bruce?
It is good to make new friends.
Will you have something to eat?"

"Oh, thank you! Thank you!"
said Jean and Bruce.

17

"Jean and Bruce," said Sally.
"We want you
to see the play house.
Come in and see it."

"Oh, this is fun!" said Jean.
"Look, Bruce.
Look at this play house."

"What a big play house!"
said Bruce.

"We like to play here,"
said Ted.

"We have to go home now,"
said Jean.

"It was fun to play with you.
I like my new friends."

"I do, too," said Bruce.

"We like you,"
said Ted and Sally.

"We like to have you
for friends."

"Good-by," said Bruce and Jean.
"Good-by," said Ted and Sally.

Jean's Father

"Sally and Ted," said Mother.
"Jean's father was here.
He wants you to go for a ride.
Do you want to go?"

"Oh, yes, Mother!"
said Sally and Ted.
"We want to go.
It will be fun to ride
with Jean's father.
Will Jean and Bruce go, too?"

"Yes," said Mother.
"You will all go."

"Here is Mr. Brown now,"
said Mother.
"Run and get in the car."

"I see Jean," said Sally.
"Bruce is in the car, too.
Come on, Ted.
Good-by, Mother."

"Good-by, Mother," said Ted.

"Good-by, Ted and Sally,"
said Mother.

"Thank you, Mr. Brown,"
said Ted and Sally.
"It is fun to ride with you."

"Father," said Bruce.
"Where are we going?"

"You will see, Bruce,"
said Mr. Brown.
"You will see."

"It will be fun!"
said Ted and Sally
and Bruce and Jean.

The Zoo

"Now," said Mr. Brown.
"Do you see where we are going?"

"It is the zoo!" said Bruce.
"Ted and Sally,
do you like the zoo?"

"Yes, yes!" said Ted.
"Oh, yes! We like the zoo,"
said Sally.

"Come, boys and girls,"
said Mr. Brown.
"We will go into the zoo."

"Look, Sally," said Ted.
"We will see all the animals."

"Oh, yes!" said Sally.
"Big animals! Little animals!
I want to see all the animals
in the zoo."

Bruce and Jean laughed.
Mr. Brown laughed, too.

They went into the zoo.

"Now," said Mr. Brown.

"There is something in the zoo
I want you to see.

There is something new
in the zoo."

"Oh, Father!" said Jean.

"What is it?

What is new in the zoo?"

"I want you to find it,"
said Jean's father.

"Something new in the zoo!"
said the boys and girls.

"We will find it."

Big Animals

"Here are the elephants,"
said Ted.
"I like elephants."

"How big they are!"
said Sally.
"They are big, big animals.'

"They are all big but one,"
said Bruce.
"One is a baby elephant."

"I see three elephants,"
said Jean.

"I see Mother Elephant,
Father Elephant,
and Baby Elephant.

But they are not new.

Father, we like the elephants.

But they are not new in the zoo."

"No, Jean," said Mr. Brown.

"The elephants are not new."

GIRAFFE

"Look at this funny animal,"
said Sally.

"Is he new in the zoo?"

"No, he is not new," said Bruce.
"But he is funny."

They all laughed
at the funny big animal.

28

"Look, Sally," said Ted.
"See the big yellow animals.
They look like cats."

"Oh, my!" said Sally.
"They do look like cats.
Are they new, Mr. Brown?
Are they new in the zoo?"

"No, Sally," said Mr. Brown.

"Bears! Bears!" said Ted.
"Look at the bears!"

"See the big brown bear,"
said Bruce.
"Look, Ted.
Look at the big brown bear."

"I see a baby bear, too,"
said Sally.
"Look, Jean.
See the funny baby bear."

"A man is coming,"
said Mr. Brown.

"The bears are going
to have something to eat."

"Up, up!" said the man
to the big brown bear.

And up went the big bear.

"Oh, oh, oh!" said Ted.
"He looks like a big brown dog!"

Little Animals

"Look, Sally," said Jean.
"Here are the monkeys.
Do you like monkeys?"

"Oh, yes!" said Sally.
"They are funny little animals.
See the monkeys jump and play.
They have fun."

"Ted," said Bruce.
"Look at this monkey.
See what he can do."

"Oh, I see!" said Ted.
"He is funny.
Is he new, Mr. Brown?
Is he new in the zoo?"

"No," said Mr. Brown
"The monkey is not new."

"Oh! Oh! Oh!" said Jean.
"Here it is.
Here is something new
in the zoo!
What is it, Father?
What is this animal?"

"It is the panda,"
said Mr. Brown.
"Yes, this animal is new
in the zoo.
Do you like the panda?"

"Oh, yes, yes!"
said the boys and girls.

34

C296734

"Look at the pandas play,"
said Sally.

"They have fun."

"They like to eat," said Jean.
"See the pandas eat."

"The pandas have a good home
in the zoo," said Mr. Brown.
"They like it here."

Pandas

"The pandas are red," said Jean.

"Yes," said Sally.
"They are red and black."

"I see yellow on the pandas,"
said Bruce.
"I see brown, too."

"Yes," said Mr. Brown.
"They are red and black,
and yellow and brown.
They are pretty little animals."

36

"There are four pandas in all,"
said Ted.

"One, two, three, four pandas.
I like the little pandas."

"Oh, they are pretty!" said Sally.
"Pretty little pandas!
They want to be friends.
I like you, little pandas."

"Mr. Brown," said Sally.
"I have a toy panda at home.
But it is black and white."

"Yes, Sally," said Mr. Brown.
"There are
black and white pandas.
The toy ones are
all black and white.
But the little red animals
are pandas, too."

Good-by to the Zoo

"Now, boys and girls,"
said Mr. Brown.
"We have to go home."

"Father," said Jean.
"I like the pandas best."

"I do, too," said Sally.

39

"Ted," said Bruce.
"What do you like best
in the zoo?"

"I like the bears
and elephants best," said Ted.
"What do you like best, Bruce?"

"The monkeys," said Bruce.
"I like the monkeys best.
But it was fun
to find the pandas."

"Thank you, Mr. Brown,"
said Ted and Sally.

"Something new in the zoo
was fun."

"Did you like the pandas?"
said Mr. Brown.

"Oh, yes, we did!" said Sally.
"It was fun to come to the zoo.
Thank you, Mr. Brown.
Thank you."

Jump or Jiggle

Frogs jump,
Caterpillars hump.

Worms wiggle,
Bugs jiggle.

Rabbits hop,
Horses clop.

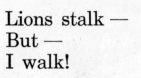

Mice creep,
Deer leap.

Puppies bounce,
Kittens pounce.

Lions stalk —
But —
I walk!

Jean and the Puppy

A Name for Puppy

"Come on, puppy," said Jean.
"Run with me.
Here we go, puppy."

"Oh, Jean!" said Bruce.
"You said 'puppy.'
Your puppy must have a name.
You must get a name
for your puppy."

"Yes, Bruce," said Jean.

"I want a name for my puppy.

But I do not like
the names you gave me.

I do not like
the names Mother gave me.

I do not like
the names Father gave me.

My puppy must have a name.

But it must be a good name."

A man came.
"Little girl," he said.
"You have a pretty puppy.
What is his name?"

"Oh! Oh! Oh!" said Jean.
"I do not have a name
for my puppy."

"My! My!" said the man.
"He must have a name.
You must get a name
for your pretty puppy."

"I will," said Jean.

"See, Jean," said Bruce.
"The puppy must have a name."

"Yes, Bruce," said Jean.
"But where will I get
a good name?"

"Do you like the name
of Ted's dog?" said Bruce.

"Oh, yes!" said Jean.
"I like the name of Ted's dog.
'Boots' is a good name.
Where did Ted get
the name 'Boots' for his dog?"

Ted and Sally

"Look, Jean," said Bruce.
"Here come Ted and Sally now."

"Hello, Sally! Hello, Ted!"
said Jean and Bruce.

"Hello!" said Ted and Sally.
"We have come to play
with you."

"Good! Good!" said Jean.
"Come into the house."

"Ted," said Bruce.
"Jean has no name for her puppy.
He must have a name."

"Oh, yes!" said Ted and Sally.
"The puppy must have a name."

"I gave Jean names
for the puppy," said Bruce.
"Father gave her names.
Mother gave her names.
But she did not like one
of the names we gave her."

"No, I did not like the names,"
said Jean.

"I want a good name
for my puppy.

I want a good name like 'Boots.'
Ted, where did you get
the name 'Boots' for your dog?"

Ted laughed.
"Look at his feet, Jean,"
said Ted.

"Do you see the black boots
on his feet?"

"Oh, I see!" said Jean.
"He has boots on his feet!"

50

Jean and Bruce
and Ted and Sally
looked at Boots.

They all laughed.

"Jean, Jean!" said Sally.
"Look at your puppy's feet.
He has no boots on his feet.
But he has mittens.
Do you see the white mittens
on your puppy's feet?"

"My! My!" said Jean.
"I do see the mittens."

"Name your puppy 'Mittens',"
said Sally.

"Do you like the name 'Mittens'
for your puppy?"

Jean looked at Sally.
Jean looked at the puppy.
Then she laughed.
"Yes! Yes! Yes!" she said.
"He has mittens on his feet.
I will name the puppy 'Mittens.'
Oh, thank you, Sally!"

Mittens Is His Name

"Here, Mittens!" said Jean.
"Come here, Mittens!"

The puppy ran to Jean.
"Look!" said Jean.
"My puppy has a name.
He likes his name, too."

Then the boys and girls
laughed and laughed.
"I am happy," said Jean.
"We are all happy," said Ted.

Mittens was happy, too.

"I am happy about this,"
said Bruce.

"I gave Jean names and names.
But she did not like the names
I gave her.

I am happy about this name.
'Mittens' is a good name."

"Yes, it is," said Jean.

"Sally gave me a good name
for my puppy."

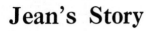

Jean's Story

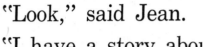

"Look," said Jean.
"I have a story about mittens.
It is about boots, too.
I will read it to you."

"Oh, do, Jean!" said Sally.
"Do read the story to us."

"Read it," said Ted and Bruce.
"Read the story to us."

"The story is about boots
and mittens," said Jean.
"But they are not dogs.
The mittens in the story
are black mittens.
The boots are red boots.
I will read the story."

Black Mittens

Once there was a little boy.
He lived on a farm.

Hens and chickens lived
on the farm.
Ducks and pigs lived there.
Horses and cows lived there.

Grandmother and Grandfather
lived on the farm, too.

Once the little boy's father
said to him,

"Grandmother is going to make
something for you.

Go and see Grandmother about it."

Little Boy ran to Grandmother.
"Oh, Grandmother!" he said.
"What are you going to make
for me?"

"Mittens!" said Grandmother.
"Good black mittens, my boy!"

"Oh, my!" said Little Boy.
"They will be good mittens.
Grandmother, will you put red
on the black mittens for me?"

Grandmother did put red
on the black mittens for him.
Little Boy was happy.

"Thank you, Grandmother,"
said Little Boy.
"Thank you for the mittens."

Red Boots and Black Mittens

"Little Boy," said Grandfather.
"I have something for you, too."

"Is it a toy?" said Little Boy.
"Do you have toys for me?"

"No, not toys," said Grandfather.
"Good red boots are not toys."

"Look at them!" said Little Boy.
"Look at my red boots!"

"Put them on," said Grandfather.
"Put on your red boots."

Little Boy put his red boots on.
He put on his black mittens, too.

"I must tell Grandmother
about my red boots,"
said Little Boy.

Away he ran to tell Grandmother
about his red boots.
"I have my black mittens on, too,"
he said.

Little Boy ran to his big dog.
"Look here, Big Dog!" he said.
"See my boots and mittens!
We must go and tell
all the animals about them."

Away went Little Boy,
splash, splash in his red boots.
Big Dog went, too.

All at once Big Dog looked down.
"Look at this!" he said.
"It is one of Little Boy's mittens.
Little Boy lost the mitten."

Away ran Big Dog with the mitten.

Big Dog gave the mitten
to Little Boy.

"Oh, my!" said Little Boy.
"I lost one of my mittens.
My mittens must not get lost.
Where can I put them?"

"Put them in your red boots,"
said Big Dog.
"Then they will not get lost."

Little Boy put his black mittens
in his red boots.

Where Are the Mittens?

Little Boy saw a hen.
"Look, Hen," he said.
"Look at my boots and mittens."

The hen saw the red boots,
but she did not see the mittens.
"Cluck! Cluck!" she said.
"Little Boy! Little Boy!
Where are your mittens?
Have you lost your mittens?"

But Little Boy laughed.
Then he ran on.

The hen went to the duck.
"Duck," she said.
"Did you see Little Boy?"

"Quack! Quack! No! No!"
said the duck.
"I did not see him."

"He is a funny boy," said the hen.
"He said he had mittens.
But I looked and looked,
and he had no mittens."

"My! My!" said the duck.
"He must have lost his mittens."

"Then we must help him
find his mittens," said the hen.
"Come on, duck."

Away went the hen and duck.
They saw the pig.

"Oh, Pig!" said the duck.
"Little Boy has lost his mittens.
Do you know where they are?"

"No, I do not know
where they are," said the pig.

"Will you help us find them?"
said the hen and duck.
"Oh, yes!" said the pig.
"I like Little Boy.
I will help you find
Little Boy's mittens."

Away went the hen and the duck
and the pig.

They saw the horse.

"Hello, Horse!" they said.

"Do you know where
Little Boy's mittens are?"

But the horse did not know.

Then they saw the cow.

"Cow," they said.

"Little Boy has lost his mittens.

Will you help us find them?"

"Oh, yes!" said the cow.

"I will help you."

Funny, Funny Boy

The hen and the duck,
the pig and the horse,
all went with the cow.

They looked and looked
for Little Boy's mittens.
But no mittens did they find.

"Oh, my!" said the cow.
"We must go back to the house.
We must tell Little Boy's father.
He can find the mittens."

Back to the house went the animals.

Then Little Boy saw the animals.
He ran to them.
"Where are you going?" he said.

"Oh, Little Boy!" said the cow.
"We can not find your mittens.
We are going to the house
to tell your father."

"Find my mittens!" said Little Boy.
"I do not want you
to find my mittens.
I have not lost my mittens."

"Oh! Oh! Oh!" said the hen.
"You said for me to look
at your mittens.
But you had no mittens!"

Little Boy laughed and laughed.
"Here are my mittens," he said.

There were the mittens.
They were in Little Boy's boots!

Then all the animals laughed.
"What a funny boy you are!"
they said.
"Put your mittens on.
What good are mittens
in your boots?"

Little Boy put on the mittens.
Then away he went in his red boots.
Splash, splash, splash!
All the animals went with him.
Splash, splash, splash!

"That is the story of the boots
and mittens," said Jean.

"That is all of the story."

"I like it," said Ted and Bruce.

"That is a good story,"
said Sally.

"Thank you, Jean.

Thank you for the story."

Books To Read

Animals in the Zoo

"Father," said Ted.
"We had a good time at the zoo."

"I know you did, Ted,"
said Father.
"What animals did you like best?"

"I liked the bears
and elephants best," said Ted.
"But I liked the pandas, too."

72

"Oh, Father!" said Sally.
"We did have a good time.
I liked the pandas best
of all the animals.
But the pandas in the zoo
were not like my toy panda.
The pandas in the zoo
were red and black
and yellow and brown."

"The zoo was fun," said Ted.
"Mr. Brown said
there was something new
in the zoo.
He did not tell us what it was.
But he gave us time to find it.
It was the pandas.
They have a new home in the zoo."

Tell Us about Pandas

"Father," said Sally.
"Where did the pandas live
before they came to the zoo?
They must have had a home
before they came to the zoo."

"Yes, Sally," said Father.
"They came to the zoo
on a boat and a train.
Do they like to live in the zoo?"

"They must like it," said Ted.
"They look happy in the zoo."

"Father," said Sally.

"Tell us about the home
of the pandas.

Did they have a good home
before they came to the zoo?"

"Sally," said Father.

"I do not know much
about pandas.

I do not know much
about where they lived.

But I know where
we can find out about it."

"Oh, we know!" said Ted and Sally.

"May we go with you?"

"Yes, you may," said Father.

Books about Animals

"Father," said Sally.
"I like to come here.
I like to get books to read."

"I do, too," said Ted.
"They have good books.
Father, do they have books
about pandas?"

"We will see, Ted," said Father.

"How do you do?" said Father.

"Ted and Sally went to the zoo
and saw the new pandas there.

We do not know much about them.

May we see some books
about the red pandas?"

"Oh, yes!" she said.

"I put out some books
about the little pandas.

I want boys and girls
to come and get the books."

"Look, Ted and Sally," said Father.
"Look at this panda.
We can not take this book
home with us.
But we can look at it here."

"He is a pretty panda,"
said Sally.
"Look at his red back.
Look at his four black feet.
He is in a book,
but I want to play with him."

"Ted and Sally," said Father.
"Here are some books
that we can take home.
Find the ones you like best."

"I like this one," said Sally.

"Here are two that I like,"
said Ted.
"Here is a book about a monkey.
May I take this one, too?"

"Yes, take that, too," said Father.
"We will take home
four good books."

Father Reads a Story

"Father," said Sally.
"Will you read this book to us?
It is a story about pandas."

"Yes, Sally, I will," said Father.

Just then Mother came in.

"Mother," said Ted and Sally.
"You are just in time.
Father is going to read a story
about pandas."

Here is the story.

Pandas at Home

Once there was a little panda.
His home was far, far away.

He had a mother and a father.
There were little pandas
for him to play with.

Little Panda was happy
in his home far away.

Little Panda liked to play
in the trees.
"I can climb," he said.
"See me climb up this big tree."

Up, up the big tree he went.
Then down the tree he came
on his four black feet.

"I know how to climb,"
said Little Panda.
"I can climb all the big trees."

A Pet Panda

Boys and girls live in homes
far, far away, too.

They like the pandas.

They like to get them for pets.

One day a boy called
to Little Panda.

"Come here, Little Panda,"
he said.

"I have something you like.
Climb down and see."

The boy called and called.
But the panda did not climb down.

"Look, Little Panda,"
said the boy.
"Here is something
you like very much."

Little Panda looked.
He did see something
he liked very much.
Down the tree he came.
He ran to the boy.

84

"Now, then," said the boy.
"We are friends.
Do you want to come home
with me?
You could live in my house.
You could have a good home.
You could have good things to eat.
Will you come, Little Panda?"

Little Panda wanted
good things to eat.
He went home with the boy.

The New Home

Little Panda was very happy
in his new home.
He had good things to eat.
He had a good bed.

The boy liked his new pet.
He called Little Panda
his little red bear cat.
"You look like a cat,"
he said.
"And you look like a bear, too.
I like you very, very much."

Other boys saw the pet panda.
One day they said,
"We want pet pandas, too.
How can we get pandas for pets?"

The boy said,
"We will take my little panda
back to the big trees.
He will tell the other pandas
about his good home.
They will want to come home
with him."

"Come on," said the boys.
"We will go now."

The boy put Little Panda
up in a big tree.

Little Panda called
to all the other little pandas.
"I have a new home," he said.
"I have good things to eat.
You could come with me.
You could be a pet.
You could have good things
to eat, too.
Do you want to come?"

The other little pandas
looked at the boys.

"Climb down, little pandas,"
said the boys.
"We have something for you.
It is good to eat.
Come down and get it."

Out of the trees
came the other little pandas.
They liked the good things to eat.
They went home with the boys.

All the boys were happy.
Some little girls had pandas,
and they were happy, too.

"Pandas," said the boys and girls.
"You are good pets.
We like you very, very much."

All the pandas were happy
in the new home.
They live there now
with the boys and girls.

"That is all of the story,"
said Father.

"I wish I could go far away,"
said Ted.
"I wish I could see
where the pandas live."

"I do, too," said Sally.
"But we can not go."

"No," said Mother.
"But you can go to the zoo
and see the pandas there."

"Oh, yes!" said Ted and Sally.
"We can go to the zoo
and see the pandas.
And we can read about them
in books."

Ted Reads a Story

"Ted and Sally," said Father,
"We must take the books back."

"Yes, Father," said Ted.
"But may I read this story
to you before we go?"

"Oh, yes!" said Father.
"Do read it to us."

"The name of the story
is 'Baby Monkey and the Elephant,'"
said Ted.

Here is the story.

Baby Monkey and the Elephant

Once there was a baby monkey.
He lived in a tree with his mother.

One day his mother said,
"Good-by, Baby Monkey.
I am going to get
some good things for us to eat.
Be a good little monkey
and stay in the tree."

Baby Monkey saw his mother
climb down and go away.

Baby Monkey looked down
from the tree.

All at once he saw
a funny animal.

"I never saw him before,"
said Baby Monkey.

"What animal is that?"

Baby Monkey looked down
at the funny animal.

"See his funny long nose,"
said Baby Monkey.
"I never saw a nose
like that before."

Baby Monkey looked and looked.
Then all at once,
he came down from the tree.
He had to see
that funny long nose.

Baby Monkey laughed
and laughed and laughed.
"Oh, oh, oh!" he said.
"Who are you?
Where did you get
that funny long nose?"

"I am Little Elephant,"
said the animal.
"And my nose is not funny."

The Elephant's Long Nose

"I have a very good nose,"
said Little Elephant.
"I can do things with my nose.
I can blow with it.
Look at this.
See me blow with my nose."

"Oh, my!" said Baby Monkey.

"I can do other things
with my nose," said Little Elephant.
"I can put it up in this tree
and get things to eat with it.
Look at this."

"Oh, I can do that!"
said Baby Monkey.
"This is the way I do it."

"Here is something
you can not do,"
said Little Elephant.
"I can take you up.
Then down you go!"

"Can you do this?"
said Little Elephant.
"Oh, yes!" said Baby Monkey.
"Look at the way I do it."

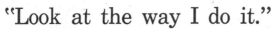

Baby Monkey and the River

Little Elephant went to the river.

"Now see me blow with my nose," he said.

"This is fun."

"I wish I could blow like that," said Baby Monkey.

Then into the river
went Little Elephant.
   Splash! Splash! Splash!
   "See me swim!" he said.
   "Come on in, Baby Monkey.
   Come in and swim."

Baby Monkey wanted
to swim very much.
   Into the river he went.

Down, down, down
went Baby Monkey!
All of Baby Monkey
you could see was his nose.

Then he came up,
and he had to blow and blow
with his nose!

But Baby Monkey was afraid.
He was very much afraid.

"Oh, oh, oh!" said Baby Monkey.
"I wish I were back in the tree.
My mother said,
'Stay in the tree.'
I wish I were in the tree now!
I must do something.
What can I do?
Oh! Oh! I am afraid."

All at once some one
took Baby Monkey out of the river.
"Who is it?" said Baby Monkey.
Then he saw who it was.
It was his mother!

She said,
"You must never go into the river!
Don't you know
baby monkeys can not swim?"

"I want to swim," said Baby Monkey.
"And I want a long nose
like Little Elephant."

"Now, now!" said his mother.
"You don't want a nose
like Little Elephant.
You have a good nose.
And you can do things
Little Elephant can never do.
You can not swim.
But you can climb trees!"

Holding Hands

Elephants walking
Along the trails

Are holding hands
By holding tails.

Trunks and tails
Are handy things

When elephants walk
In circus rings.

Elephants work
And elephants play

And elephants walk
So big and gray.

And when they walk
It never fails

They're holding hands
By holding tails.

Little Dog Mittens

Jean and Bruce

"Look, Ted!" said Sally.
"Here come Jean and Bruce.
They are running.
What are they running
like that for?"

"I don't know," said Ted.
"But they are running fast.
Oh, Jean! Oh, Bruce!
Come in! Come in!"

Into Ted and Sally's house
ran Jean and Bruce.

"My! My!" said Sally.
"You were running fast.
What were you running fast
like that for?"

"Oh, oh, oh!" said Jean.
"We have something big
to tell you!"

"What is it?" said Ted and Sally.

"Jean and I are going far away,"
said Bruce.

"We are going on a big ship.
Mother and Father and Jean
and I are going on the big ship.
Oh, it will be fun!"

"Will you be away a long time?"
said Sally.

"We will be away all summer,"
said Jean.
"I wish you were going, too."

"Thank you, Jean," said Sally.
"I know you will have
a happy summer."

"You will have fun
on the big ship," said Ted.

"Oh, Jean!" said Ted.

"What will you do with Mittens?
Can he go on the ship?"

"No, we can not take Mittens
with us," said Jean.

"He is going to stay
with our grandfather.

Grandfather Brown has a farm.

Mittens will stay all summer
on the farm."

"That will be fun for Mittens,"
said Ted.

"He will like to stay on a farm."

"Will you come to our ship
and see us go?" said Bruce.

"Oh, yes!" said Ted and Sally.

Good-by

The day came
for the big ship to go.
Down to the ship
went Ted and Sally
and Mother and Father.

Mr. Brown and Mrs. Brown
and Jean and Bruce were there.

"Look, Ted and Sally!"
called Bruce.
"That is our ship!"

Jean and Bruce took
Ted and Sally on the ship.

"How big it is!" said Ted.

"Come," said Bruce.
"We will take you over the ship.
You will see just how big it is.
We went on this ship once before.
We like it very much."

Ted and Sally went over the ship
with Jean and Bruce.

"Here are our beds," said Jean.

"My! My!" said Sally.
"The beds look just like beds
at home.
I like this ship."

"Here is where we play,"
said Bruce.

"We can play here every day."

"Oh, Bruce!" said Ted.

"It will be fun to come up here
every day and play.

You will have a good time."

"Jean," said Sally.
"Did Mittens go to the farm?"

"Yes," said Jean.
"Grandfather took him
to the farm.
I wish I could take Mittens
with me on the ship."

"Mittens will like the farm
very much," said Sally.
"He will have fun all summer
on the farm."

"Yes, I know he will," said Jean.

Then it was time
for the ship to go.

Ted and Sally saw it go.

"Good-by, Jean and Bruce,"
they called.

It was a fast ship.
Over the water it went.
It was not long
before Ted and Sally
could not see it at all.

"I wish Jean had let Mittens
stay with us," said Ted.
"Boots would let Mittens
stay in his dog house."

"Yes, he would," said Father.
"But it is good for a dog
to stay on a farm.
Mittens will have fun
running all over the farm."

"He can run fast," said Ted.
"Mittens will have
a happy summer on the farm."

Summer at the Farm

Mittens liked the farm.
Every day he would go running,
running all over the farm.
Then he would have to stop.

"My!" said Grandfather Brown.
"I never saw a dog
who could run so much.
Jean would like to see you
run so fast.
But you do have to stop,
don't you, Mittens?
You may come with me now.
I will let you help me
find the eggs."

It was fun for Mittens
to be on the farm.

There were so many things
for a dog to see.

There were so many things
for a dog to do.

Mittens liked the things
he could do on the farm.

Best of all, he liked the rides.

There were so many rides
he could have on the farm.

There was the ride to the garden.

Mittens liked that.

Every day Mittens had a ride
when Mr. Brown went to the garden.

"Here!" said Mr. Brown.
"Jump in and ride."
Mittens jumped in
and away he went.

Mittens was not a big dog.
He was too little to see
all the things he wanted to see.
But when he had a ride,
he could see all about him.

A Ride Every Day

Mittens liked the little rides
to the garden.
But he liked long rides, too.
Every day he had a long ride.
Mittens could tell
when it was time for his ride.
When it was time, he ran
and looked down the road.

"Yes, Mittens," said Mr. Brown.
"It is about time now."
Then Mittens ran down the road
to get his ride.

Down the road went Mittens.
He came to a hill.
Up the hill he went.
Then he sat down by the road.

Yes, there was the car.
Mittens could see it.
It was Mr. Good
in his blue car.

The blue car came up the hill.
It stopped by Mittens.

"Jump in, Mittens," said Mr. Good.
"We must be on our way.
I have so many letters
to take to all the farms."

Mittens jumped in.
Away they went.

A Letter from Jean

"I have many, many letters
every day," said Mr. Good.
"I must take them to the farms."

Mittens heard Mr. Good.
But Mittens had other things to do.
He wanted to look and look.
That was one of the best things
about a ride.

Mittens put two feet up
on the door of the car.
He looked and looked.

Down the road went Mittens
and Mr. Good in the blue car.

There were so many things
for Mittens to see.

He saw some horses.

He saw some pigs.

Once he saw a big black cow
by the road.

Not far away, he heard a train.
"Choo-choo!   Choo-choo!"
said the train.

Mittens thought it was fun
to ride with Mr. Good in the car.

"Now, Mittens," said Mr. Good.
"Here is where you live.
Take the letters to Mr. Brown."

Mittens jumped out of the car.
Mr. Good gave him three letters.

"Good-by, Mittens," said Mr. Good.
Mr. Good went down the road
in his blue car.
He had letters to take
to other farm houses.

Mittens took the three letters
to Mr. Brown.

"Mittens," said Mr. Brown.
"Here is a letter from Jean.
I thought we would get
a letter from Jean.
I will read it to you."

Grandfather Brown did read
the letter to Mittens.
"Be a good dog, Mittens,"
said the letter from Jean.

The Farm Wagon

One day Mittens had a new ride.
This time it was a ride
on the big farm wagon.

"Come on," said Mr. Brown.
"Up you go!"

Mr. Brown put Mittens up
on the big farm wagon.
Away went the big horses.
Away went Mittens and Mr. Brown.

It was fun to ride
on the big farm wagon.
Mittens liked to look down
at the horses.
He liked to look down
at the road.

He saw a hen in the road.
She had little chickens with her.

"Cluck! Cluck! Cluck!"
said the hen to her chickens.
Out of the road she ran.
Away went the little chickens.

130

The wagon came to a little river.

Over the river they went.

Mittens could look down
and see the water.

He saw four big white ducks
in the water.

He saw some little yellow ducks
in the water, too.

"Quack! Quack! Quack!"
said the four white ducks
in the water.

Mittens saw a boy in a boat.
"My! My!" thought Mittens.
"I wish I could ride in a boat.
I never took a ride on the water."

Mittens went to the back
of the wagon.
He wanted to get a good look
at that boat.
But the wagon went on,
and he could not see the boat.

Look Out, Mittens!

Mittens could not see the boat.
But there were other things
to see from the back of the wagon.

It was fun to see the road
from the back of the wagon.
They were going up a hill now.
Up, up, up they went.

Mittens looked down at the road.
Then all at once
the road came up at Mittens.
That was the way it looked
to him.
But it was Mittens
that went down to the road.
Down, down he went.

The wagon went on.

Mr. Brown thought Mittens was
at the back of the wagon.

But Mittens was not on the wagon.

Mittens was on the road.

Mittens did not know
what to think of this.

He jumped up and looked about him.

He could not see the wagon.

He could not see Mr. Brown.

Mittens did not know what to do.

Where Are You Going?

Mittens sat down by the road.
He sat and looked up the road.
He looked down the road.
Just then he heard a car coming.

Up the hill came the car.
It stopped by Mittens.

The man in the car
looked at Mittens.

"Hello, little dog!" he said.

"Who are you?

Where do you think you are going?"

Mittens just looked at the man.

He wanted the man
to open the car door.

And the man did open the door.

Mittens jumped in.

Down the road they went.

Mittens put two feet up
on the car door.

He looked at the trees.

He looked at the horses and cows.

He looked at the pigs.

He looked at all the animals
when they went by a farm.

Mittens was happy.

He thought he was going home.

But Mittens was not going home.
Before long, the car stopped.
Mittens jumped out.
He looked about him.
They were at a farm house.
But he was not at home.

"I don't like this," said Mittens.
He ran back to the road.
Mittens did not know
where he was.
He was lost.

Little Lost Dog

Mittens sat down by the road.
He saw a car coming.
It was a big, big car.

Mittens saw boys and girls
in the big car.
They were going home.

"Look, look!" said a boy.
"There is a little dog!"

"Just look at him!" said a girl
"He has pretty white feet.
Hello, little dog! Hello!"

All the boys and girls
looked at Mittens.
But the boys and girls
had to get home.
The big car did not stop.

Mittens did not know
what to think of that.
He wanted to ride
with the boys and girls.
He liked boys and girls.
And he wanted to get home, too.

Night was coming.
Mittens must get home.
He had to get home before night.
He went running down the road.

Night came.

Mittens did not like the cars now.
They came at him out of the night.

He was afraid.
He ran away from the road.

Mittens ran and ran.
Then he came to a cow.
He stopped to look at the cow.

Then other cows came.
All the cows looked at Mittens.
The cows did not like him.
Mittens was afraid and he ran on.

A Night Away from Home

Mittens came to a farm house.
He wanted something to eat.
So he went to the door
of the farm house.

He put two feet up on the door.
That was the way
he did at home.
That was the way he said,
"Let me in.
Do let me come in."

A little old man came
to open the door of the farm house.
"My, my! Little dog!" he said.
"Who are you?
What do you want?"

Mittens just looked
at the little old man.

146

Then a little old woman
came to the open door.

"Let him come in," said the woman.
"He wants something to eat.
Come in, little dog.
You are just in time
to have something to eat."

"Eat! Eat!" thought Mittens.
"I think I know what that is."
And into the house he went.

The little old woman gave
Mittens something good to eat.

Then the little old woman said,
"There is a bed for you.
You must go to bed."

So Mittens went to bed
in the farm house.

"Get up, little dog,"
said the little old woman.

"I don't know your name.

But here is something good
for you to eat."

Mittens liked the little old woman.
He liked the little old man.
But this was not his home.
"Do open that door," he thought.
They did open the door.
Back to the road went Mittens.

149

Going Home

Mittens sat down by the road.
He saw a car coming.
But it did not stop to let him ride.

Then three other cars went by.
But not one of them would stop.
Mittens did not know
what to think of this.

Mittens sat down by the road.
He heard a car coming.
Then he saw a blue car stop
at a farm house.
Now the car was coming up the hill.
But it went on.

No! The blue car stopped.
It came back to Mittens.
The door of the car came open.
And this is what Mittens heard,
"Jump in, Mittens.
We must be on our way.
I have so many letters
to take to all the farms."

It was Mr. Good.

Mr. Good wanted to know
so many things.

"Where were you going, Mittens?
How did you get here?
Were you out all night?
Have you had something to eat?"

But Mittens could not tell him.

Mittens had other things to do.
He put two feet up
on the door of the car.

He looked at horses and cows.
He looked at chickens and ducks.
He looked at all the animals
on the farms.

Mr. Good stopped at farm houses
with letters.

When he stopped,
Mittens heard the old hens go,
    "Cluck! Cluck! Cluck!"
And he heard the ducks go,
    "Quack! Quack! Quack!"

The ducks were happy.
The chickens were happy.
And Mittens was happy, too.
He was going home.

A Good Little Dog

"Look, Mittens," said Mr. Good.
"We are coming to your house."

They went down one hill
and up the other hill.
Now Mittens could see it.
Yes, that was his home.

Mr. Good stopped and said,
"Here we are, Mittens.
Here are four letters."

Mittens took the four letters
and away he ran.
He was happy to be back home.

There was Grandfather Brown.
He was going to the garden.
Mittens ran to him with the letters.

"Oh, Mittens!" said Mr. Brown.
"It is good to see you.
I was afraid you were lost.
Then what would Jean think?"

Mr. Brown wanted to know this
and he wanted to know that.
But Mittens could not tell him
a thing.

So Grandfather Brown went on
to the garden.

"Jump in, Mittens," he said.

"Jump in and have a ride."

Mittens jumped in
and away they went to the garden.

It was good to be home.

"I will stay at home, too,"
thought Mittens.

And Mittens did stay
at home all summer.

When Jean came home,
she said Mittens was a good dog,
a very good little dog.

Word List

The following list contains all the new words — 114 in number — that occur in *On Four Feet*, basal first reader of *The Macmillan Readers*. The 121 words introduced in *Splash* and *Tuffy and Boots*, basal pre-primers, and *Ted and Sally*, basal primer, are repeated, making a total basal first-reader vocabulary of 235 words. With the exception of sound words and the names of characters, they are words frequently found in children's reading.

1.	23. zoo	42.	60. tell
2.	24. into	43.	61. lost
3.	animals	44. must	62.
4.	25.	name	63. saw
5.	26. elephants	45. gave	64. had
6.	baby	46. his	help
7. puppy	27.	47. of	65. know
8. where	28.	48. hello	66.
9. your	29.	49. has	67. back
10.	30. bears	her	68.
11. Jean	31.	50. feet	69. were
Bruce	32. monkeys	51. mittens	70. that
12.	33.	52. then	71. books
13. friends	34. panda	53. happy	72. time
14.	35.	54. about	liked
15.	36. black	55. read	73.
16.	pretty	us	74. live
17. new	37. four	56. once	before
18.	38. toy	lived	75. much
19.	white	57. him	may
20. Jean's	39. best	58. put	76.
21. brown	40.	59. them	77. some
22.	41.		78. take

79.
80. just
81. far
82. trees
    climb
83. day
    called
84. very
85. could
    things
86.
87. other
88.
89.
90.
91. wish
92.
93. stay
94. from
    never
95. long
    nose
96. who

97. blow
98. way
99.
100. river
101. swim
102. afraid
103.
104. took
     don't
105.
106.
107.
108. running
     fast
109.
110. ship
     summer
111. our
112.
113. over
114.
115. every
116.
117. water

118. let
     would
119. stop
     so
120. many
     garden
121. when
     jumped
122. road
123. sat
     by
124. stopped
     letters
125. heard
     door
126. thought
127.
128.
129.
130.
131.
132.
133.
134.

135. think
136.
137. open
138.
139.
140.
141.
142. night
143.
144.
145.
146. old
147. woman
148.
149.
150.
151.
152.
153.
154.
155.
156.
157.

159